Stephanie Snell Povey is and always has been a tomboy. Her greatest passions involve being a wife, mother, grandmother, educator, gardener, master builder and athlete.

A lifelong Utahn who loves to travel, she can often be found building a playhouse with her grandchildren, helping a friend cut down trees or playing her heart out on a pickleball court.

Stephanie and her husband Reed of 38 years, reside in Kaysville, Utah.

Thanks for your support!
♡ Steph

For my wonderful parents and husband who have always been my greatest cheerleaders.

To all those who have been discriminated against for any reason. May you find the hope and strength to press forward in your journey.

Stephanie Snell Povey

# You Can't Play, You're a Girl

AUSTIN MACAULEY PUBLISHERS™

LONDON • CAMBRIDGE • NEW YORK • SHARJAH

**Ordering Information**
Quantity sales: Special discounts are available on quantity purchases by corporations, associations, and others. For details, contact the publisher at the address below.

**Publisher's Cataloging-in-Publication data**
Povey, Stephanie Snell
You Can't Play, You're a Girl

ISBN 9781638298243 (Paperback)
ISBN 9781638298250 (ePub e-book)

Library of Congress Control Number: 2022914453

www.austinmacauley.com/us

First Published 2022
Austin Macauley Publishers LLC
40 Wall Street, 33rd Floor, Suite 3302
New York, NY 10005
USA

mail-usa@austinmacauley.com
+1 (646) 5125767

20230224

It is with deep gratitude I acknowledge those in the USA who labored tirelessly to pass Title lX, in 1972, and more specifically the 37 words within the law that changed my life forever.

"No person in the United States shall, on the basis of sex, be excluded from participation in, be denied the benefits of, or be subjected to discrimination under any educational program or activity receiving Federal financial assistance."

# Author's Note

The events in this book are only a few of the many stories from my childhood. I have changed the names, with the exception of my own and my parents, yet all of the characters are based on real people from my life.

I remember when I was about seven years old hearing a friend of my mother's say to her, "Stephanie is such an interesting little girl. I'm glad you get to raise her and not me!" I might have been young but I understood what she meant. I was not normal and even nice people, like my mother's friend, would not want me to be their little girl. I carried this knowledge with me for a long time.

In my youth, I experienced many difficult emotions such as fear, loneliness, anxiety, and anger. I developed frequent stomach aches and underwent many tests to discover the problem. The medical doctors found nothing. In the 1960s it was not fully understood the role that emotions can play on physical wellbeing nor the damaging effects that bullying, exclusion, and discrimination can have on both body and spirit.

Daring greatly, I share my story, hoping it may increase understanding regardless of our differences.

I especially write this book for my three beautiful daughters. My greatest hopes for them; they will always know their eternal value, feel understood and useful as their true authentic selves.

# Chapter 1

She stared into the mirror at her short, dark hair letting the water run. Tears formed in her eyes as she thought, *Why, why am I the only girl like me?* Pumping the soap dispenser, the pink powder filled her hand. Her father, who was a doctor, had taught her how easily scrapes and cuts can get infected so even though it stung and felt like sandpaper, she rubbed the soap up and down her arms. At last, she was satisfied they were clean and patted them dry.

"I can't go back out to afternoon recess, the girls will find me again." She worried and wondered how many other kids had seen what had happened. She heard voices coming closer to the bathroom and quickly hid in one of the stalls.

She had always been different. Her parents had shared many stories of how *unique* she was. In fact, before she was born her heartbeat had been slow like a boy's, so her parents decided on the name Steven. The delivery room was filled with surprise when the doctor announced, "It's a girl!" The name Steven was promptly changed to Stephanie.

It was quiet again and she hoped the bathroom was empty. Still, she was afraid to leave and sat on the toilet. Leaning over her knees, she felt the scabs and recalled the day she had slipped playing basketball. The girls had even

11

teased her about her scabby knees. "Nothing about me is normal!" she cried.

The Snell family moved to Kaysville Utah a few years before so her father could start a small medical clinic in the town. While he was becoming well known for delivering babies and helping sick people, Stephanie started elementary school and was becoming well known as the girl who acted like a boy.

Remembering her parents teaching her to think about her blessings whenever she was feeling sad, she closed her eyes and imagined all the things she loved about her life.

*I love Molly!* she thought. Steph had been thrilled when her little sister was born. She often climbed into her crib to read with her and enjoyed taking her on walks in the stroller around the neighborhood. Sometimes she would pretend that she was the mommy and Molly was her little girl.

She *loved* playing basketball with her father on the court he built in their backyard.

She *loved* working in the garden with her mother and the feel of the soil in her hands as she helped plant and weed.

She *loved* the smell of fresh-cut grass while mowing the lawn and could mow it all by herself by the time she was seven.

Suddenly, the bell rang, and it startled her back to reality. Quickly, she left the bathroom and headed to class. It seemed that everyone was laughing at her as she walked down the hall. Had all these kids seen too? She wanted to go home and never come back.

# Chapter 2

On the bus ride home Steph sat by herself. She was thankful she had worn a sweater that morning so she could hide the scratches on her arms. The neighbor boys said "Hi" as they got on the bus and she timidly waved, then turned to face the window wondering if they had seen. She had been teased since kindergarten but nothing as awful as today.

Her mind flashed back to a day several weeks before, when the teasing began to get worse. Because she had no real friends at school, she began to play marbles at recess with some of the so-called "non-sporty" boys. They didn't seem to mind if Steph hung out with them. Perhaps because they were considered weird too.

One tall boy named Gary, with a rather large head, had just drawn a circle in the dirt for them to begin the game, when a group of girls, looking for something to do, wandered over and started calling him "Egghead." Gary stood and yelled back at them, *"Sticks and stones may break my bones, but names can never hurt me!"*

A girl named Betty mimicked him, "Sticks and stones! Oh, did your mommy tell you to say that?" Betty was a girl who always wore the nicest dresses, the fanciest shoes, had the perfect hair with matching bows and was clearly the leader of the group. Gary threw his marbles on the ground angrily to which Betty and the girls heartlessly began chanting "Egghead lost his marbles! Egghead lost his marbles!"

Steph hated what they were doing and yelled at them, "Stop it, you idiots!" 'Idiot' was not a word she was allowed to use at home, but in this situation, it seemed the perfect thing to call them. Yet, it only made things worse, for after that day Betty and the girls began to torment Steph even more.

Every day, when she would try to use the restroom at recess, the girls would grab her and push her into the boy's bathroom saying, "You're going in the wrong door little boy, here's *your* bathroom!" They would also block the girl's bathroom door not allowing Steph to go in. She began trying to hold it, never going to the bathroom at school.

This was miserable!

She found the teacher's lounge had a bathroom and used it a few times until she got caught and promised never to do it again.

Besides causing the bathroom problem, Betty came up with a new nickname for her. Instead of calling her by her real first and last name, she referred to her as "Stuffy Smell." Many times, throughout the day Steph would hear, "I think there is a Stuffy Smell coming our way." Or "What is that horrible Stuffy Smell?"

For some unknown reason today, Betty had the meanest idea yet. She spotted Steph on the swings and yelled, "Look there's Stuffy Smell, let's get her." A group of five girls came racing toward her and Steph knew it meant trouble. She tried to hop out of the swing and run, but the girls were waiting. The second she landed they grabbed her while Betty ordered, "Let's pull down her skirt and make sure she's a girl!" Their fingernails dug into her skin and there was nothing she could do to stop what happened. She felt her skirt *and* her underwear go down around her knees and heard Betty squeal, "She is a girl after all!"

Steph had no idea how many kids had seen, but the thought that anyone had was humiliating to her. As she felt her arms released, she pulled up her clothing and, in a panic, ran as fast as she could to the bathroom hearing their laughter trailing behind her.

As the bus bumped along, Steph realized tears were streaming down her cheeks just recalling the experience. She used her sleeve to wipe them away trying to hide her face from her fellow passengers as she got off at her stop. Walking the rest of the way home she wondered how she would ever survive school and decided not to tell anyone, not even her parents. She was so embarrassed.

Steph heard the familiar sound of her mother's sewing machine as she walked through the door. "How was your day, honey?" her mother called.

"OK," she lied, "accept I didn't do well on my spelling test and have to do it over tomorrow." She tried to be honest about something, then asked, "But can I have a snack and play for a while before homework?"

Mrs. Snell knew her daughter struggled with reading and spelling and spent hours each week helping her study. "Yes, of course," she encouraged, "Take a break for a while and I'll work with you after dinner. Would you mind checking on Molly first while I finish this costume?"

Steph found some apples in the fridge and grabbed one then went to her sister's bedroom. Molly was sprawled out on the floor surrounded by dozens of troll dolls patiently brushing the purple-haired momma troll trying to get out the snarls. "Love you Molls!" Steph shouted, surprising her little sister and making her jump. They both giggled and Steph gave her a big hug.

"Wuv you sissy," Molly replied with a smile. Steph imagined what she would do to Betty and the girls if they ever tried to hurt Molly. "Wanna play?" Molly asked, handing her a troll.

"Maybe in a while," she answered half-heartedly. She had played trolls and dolls so many times with her little sister but didn't feel like it today. "I'm going to go change my clothes, OK?" And headed to her bedroom.

Steph *hated* wearing dresses and skirts every day to school and getting out of them was the first thing she did when she got home. Tearing off the skirt she threw it on the floor exclaiming, "I never want to wear *that* again!" Then, got a better idea. Picking it up again, she stuffed it into the back of her closet where she thought it could never be found. Putting on her comfortable pair of cut-off jeans and a t-shirt, she headed out the back door munching on the apple.

She had two neighbors who were also in the third grade. They were both boys and lived on each side of her. Their yards were all connected with no fences in between making it seem like one huge backyard.

To the right of her house lived Kenny Barnes, a thin wiry kid, who was quick like Steph. He was about her size with dark brown hair and olive skin. In fact, they were

16

sometimes mistaken for siblings, they looked so much alike. To the left was Zac Barrett. He had a more stout and muscular body, with short blond hair and fair skin that often got sunburned. He wasn't a fast sprinter like Kenny and Steph, but he could throw a football twice as far and hit home runs almost every time he got up to bat.

Zac and Kenny didn't seem to mind that Steph was a girl and neither did their parents. They were always very nice to her and treated her like she was one of the guys. Even though Steph hung out with them in their backyards, she had **never** tried to play with them at school. She wondered if Zac and Kenny had seen what had happened today?

The boys were already playing on her basketball court when she arrived and neither one of them said anything nor acted differently so she pretended nothing was wrong.

They played HORSE and Around the World until it was time for dinner. As they were saying good night to each other, Steph wanted so badly to ask them if she could start playing with them at school but didn't have the courage. While washing up for dinner, she made up her mind that tomorrow she would find Zac and Kenny at first recess and hang out with them staying as far away from the girls as possible.

After dinner, Steph quietly went to her room not wanting her parents to ask what she was doing. She had a plan. She found a pair of her knit pants with holes in the knees and placed them on her bed. Then she laid a dress from her closet on top of the pants. Her mother was busy in the kitchen, so she walked softly into the sewing room. There she found the big pair of scissors she had seen her mother use many times to cut through materials. Steph carefully cut the pants off one leg at a time a little shorter than the length of the dress. "I'm going to wear these every day." She said to herself, "They'll be perfect for playing with the boys and my underwear will never show."

That night, Steph could not sleep she was so anxious about her decision. "What if the boys made fun of her too? What if they wouldn't let her play? What if they had seen her bare bottom at recess?"

Over and over her mind would not rest and the worries gave her a stomachache. After a while, she went into her parent's bedroom. "Mom, Dad, my tummy hurts," she moaned. Her mother put down the book she was reading and asked, "Do you need to use the bathroom?" Steph told her she already had, but her father instructed her to try again, "I'll get you a glass of milk while you go," he insisted. She used the bathroom, drank the milk, then her father helped her to bed and rubbed her back until she finally drifted off to sleep.

# Chapter 3

The next morning at first recess, Steph nervously headed to the part of the playground that everyone called "The Boy's Field." She saw a large group of boys getting ready to play football and spotted Zac and Kenny among them. It took every ounce of courage she had to keep walking across the field and ask them to join in.

"What?" Ronnie Peters yelled when he heard her request, "You can't play, you're a girl!" A few of the other boys chimed in agreeing with him. Ronnie was a red-headed freckled-faced boy who was good at every sport and most of the other boys wanted to be on his team.

Steph was close to tears wondering what to do next when she heard Kenny holler, "She can be on my team. She's my neighbor and she's pretty good," he went on, "Come on guys let's play, we're wasting recess time." Steph was so relieved she could have hugged Kenny! The boys all shrugged their shoulders and started to take opposite sides of the field for the kickoff.

Within the first few plays, Steph caught a pass from Zac, dodged around Ronnie and sprinted across the makeshift endzone for a touchdown. She slammed the ball into the ground like she had seen the pros do on TV to celebrate her score. As she started back across the field Ronnie glared at her, but she didn't care. Her teammates were giving her high fives and cheering. She was a girl who had just scored a touchdown on Ronnie Peters! Steph was overjoyed and hoped it meant they would let her play every recess.

When the bell rang, her team was ahead, and they shouted as if they had won the super bowl. Feeling extremely thirsty, she ran and stood in line at the outside drinking fountain. Ronnie got right behind her and scoffed, "Football is for boys, go play hopscotch with the girls!" Steph tried to ignore him, but he started sniffing his nose and asked sarcastically, "Hey, can you guys smell that Stuffy Smell?" Lots of kids laughed at this. Betty's nickname for her was well known throughout the school and she wasn't the only one who used it.

Then Ronnie called her a name she had never heard before. "Stuffy you're such a tomboy!" She turned around in the line and stared at his red freckled face not knowing what to say. He laughed at her and then repeated, "Tomboy Stuffy, Tomboy Stuffy!" A few of the other boys joined in. With all the teasing and what had happened the day before, Steph got so angry she snapped and shoved Ronnie as hard as she could. He fell backward on the blacktop landing with his feet straight up in the air. Still ablaze with fury, she tore off his left shoe and chucked it as hard as she could into a tree!

Everyone watched and waited...and waited.

But it never came down.

Now all the kids stared at Steph and she knew there was a pretty good chance she was in trouble. Forgetting her thirst, she ran as fast as she could into the school, found her teacher Mrs. Sharp and burst out, "I need to talk to you right now!"

Her teacher was very new and young. She wore her dark hair short like Steph's and was always kind. In Steph's opinion, she was the only good thing about school because she would say nice things to her like, "You're getting so good at reading, Stephanie", and "I loved the picture you drew on your book report."

Mrs. Sharp calmed her down and walked into the hall with her as the kids were coming in. She listened quietly while Steph recounted the disaster in the drinking fountain line. Her kind face had a slight smile and Steph could tell she was understanding everything. When finished, Mrs. Sharp placed her hand on Steph's shoulder and responded, "I'm so glad you came and told me, I can tell you are very upset," then paused before continuing, "now, I would like you to wait right here while I go get Ronnie. We need to hear his side of the story and talk this out with him."

She fidgeted while waiting in the hall, hoping nobody would see her standing there. Before long, Mrs. Sharp returned followed by a red-faced Ronnie limping slightly because his sneaker was still in the tree. The two classmates stood staring at each other and Ronnie began to tell his side of the story. Surprisingly, he was very honest, even repeating the mean names he had used. It wasn't long before they were shaking hands, apologizing, and promising to be kinder to each other in the future.

As they walked back into the room and took their seats, Mrs. Sharp did the most amazing thing! She stood in front of the entire class and proceeded to instruct the students,

"Boys and girls, we must be kind to each other, and you must include each other in all activities. No one can be left out if they want to participate, especially at recess." She paused, "Do you all understand?" In unison, the class responded, "Yes, Mrs. Sharp."

Steph had always liked Mrs. Sharp but after that day she *loved* her! Now she knew the boys *had* to let her play!

When Steph got home from school, she went straight to the bookshelf where her family kept the World Book Encyclopedia set. Reaching for the book with the letter T she began to look up the word tomboy. It wasn't there. "Maybe it's a swear word?" she whispered.

Her mother had been watching with interest and questioned her, "What are you looking up?" Steph hesitated, then asked, "Mom, is tomboy a swear word?" Her mother smiled.

"No, honey, but I think you'll have better luck finding it in the dictionary."

She got out their family dictionary and sure enough, it was there! It stated, *"A tomboy is an energetic girl who loves the outdoors, playing sports and other activities that are considered to be boyish."*

Steph was shocked. "That sounds just like me! I am a tomboy!" She was puzzled. "What's wrong with a girl being energetic, loving to be outdoors and playing sports?" she murmured, "Why would it be a bad thing to be a tomboy?"

Concerned by what she saw her mother asked, "What's going on Steph?" Realizing she needed to answer truthfully, Steph decided right then not to hide what was going on anymore.

Sitting down, she began to cry and described for her mother all that had been going on at school; the years of teasing; the name-calling; the events of that day with Ronnie and she even told her about Betty and the girls pulling down her underwear to see if she really was a girl.

Steph told her mother *everything* and it felt wonderful not to have any more secrets.

With tears in her eyes, her mother apologized, "Oh Steph I'm so sorry, I feel terrible, Dad and I had no idea this was going on!" Then declared, "I'm going to talk to your teacher *and* the principal about all of this. It has to stop!" She held Steph close. "I'm so proud of you for having the courage to go to school every day." Then paused, "I hope you'll always do the things that make you feel happy." Then she pulled back and looked Steph straight in the eyes. "Now promise me you will always tell me everything no matter what!"

Steph stared at her mother. "I promise, Mom. I'm sorry I didn't say anything to you and Dad. I was trying not to be a tattle tale." Then tearfully she pleaded, "Mom, why am I so different than all the other girls?"

Wrapping her up again they cried together. After several minutes, her mother finally answered, "Sweetheart, I believe there are other girls like you, you just haven't met them yet."

They visited together for almost an hour. Steph couldn't remember ever feeling so close to her mom or ever staying in her dress this long after school. When she realized this, she laughed. "I'm going to get this off, OK?" Her mother grinned and Steph was halfway to her room when she suddenly remembered her promise. "Oh wait!" she shouted, pulling up her dress to reveal her homemade shorts. "One more thing I forgot to tell you about. I cut off my green pants to make shorts for under my dress."

Her mother chuckled. "I think I should put a hem on those so they look a little nicer," then added, "and perhaps we should make you a couple more pairs of shorts for when those get dirty and need to be washed?"

Steph couldn't believe her ears! Her mother wasn't mad, *and* she was going to make more! From then on, she always wore clean, nicely hemmed shorts under her dresses every day and no one said anything about it.

Her mother kept her word and spoke with the principal about the teasing and the horrible day. Betty and the girls had to apologize to her in the hall which was awkward but at least they stayed away from her after that.

She still got called tomboy a lot and sometimes she heard the name Stuffy Smell and some laughing, but now she played on the boy's field at every recess.

For the most her school life got better, that is until the day when the worst thing possible happened.

# Chapter 4

Steph was screaming as she came through the back door after school, "Mooooom!" Her mother came quickly into the kitchen holding her finger to her lips and shushing her, "Be quiet, you'll wake up your little sister." Then taking her by the arm whispered, "Let's go out back and talk."

She followed her mother outside to their deck and blurted it out, half yelling, half crying, "Mrs. Sharp isn't my teacher anymore! Today was her last day!"

Her mother comforted her, "I knew this day was coming sweetheart." Steph sputtered in disbelief, "You mean you knew about this?"

"Well," her mom revealed, "I spoke with Mrs. Sharp at the Valentine's Day party and she informed me that she's having a baby."

"I know about that, Mom, she told us, but why can't she be my teacher anymore?"

"Because, when a woman teacher is going to have a baby," her mother spoke slowly choosing her words carefully, "and the baby starts to show in her tummy the school district makes her quit teaching."

Steph's mouth flew open. "Why?" Then fired question after question at her mother. "Why did they make that rule?

What's wrong with a baby showing in her tummy? Why can't she keep teaching if she wants to?" Steph's mother tried her best to answer every question, but no matter what she said none of the reasons made sense to her.

Finally, her mother asked, "Do you know who your new teacher is?"

"Her name is Mrs. Davis, and she's as big as Merlin Olsen!" Steph announced. Her mother smiled. She knew Merlin Olsen was a professional football player for the Los Angeles Rams and one of her daughter's favorite players to watch because he was from Utah.

"I know you will miss Mrs. Sharp so much," she comforted, "But I'm certain you'll grow to love Mrs. Davis in the same way." Steph's mom was usually right about stuff like this, but she had a gut feeling this time she was wrong.

The next day at school was horrible! First, Mrs. Davis told them to get out their language arts workbooks. Mrs. Sharp hadn't used them since the first of the year and Steph had no idea where hers was. "I can't find mine." She reported, peering into the mouth of her desk looking everywhere. Suddenly, the entire contents were being dumped on the floor in front of her.

Startled, she looked up to see a towering Mrs. Davis standing above her snidely pointing. "There it is!" It had been smashed into the very back and its soft pages were folded and torn. "Now, quickly pick everything up so we can begin!"

Steph wanted to cry. She couldn't believe a teacher could be so rude! As she was cleaning up, listening to some snickering from the back of the room, Gary and Kenny came to her aid and soon everything was put away. "Thank you," she mouthed under her breath not wanting to interrupt her new teacher.

"I suggest you all get accustomed to using these workbooks again for the rest of the school year!" Mrs. Davis proclaimed.

Later in the morning as Steph was coming in from first recess, she stopped, bent over to take off one of her shoes and dump some dirt into the trash can. Mrs. Davis spied her and in front of the entire class shouted, "Young lady, what are you doing with shorts on under your dress?" Steph tried to explain that she wears them so she can play sports with the boys at recess, but before she could finish Mrs. Davis corrected her. "Miss Stephanie Snell, you are a girl, and it is NOT lady like for a girl to play sports with the boys." then she demanded, "Now, you will need to take those shorts off at once!" And pointed to the classroom door.

Something was in her throat that made it hard to swallow. As she walked down the hall into the girl's bathroom she burst into tears and yelled out loud, "Why did Mrs. Sharp have to quit!" Then bellowed even louder, "This isn't fair!"

She went home in tears not even wanting to play with Zac and Kenny. Marching to her room, she heard her mother call out, "Steph is that you?" When no answer was given her mother appeared in the doorway now aware something was wrong. "What happened sweetie?" Her mother approached and sat on the bed.

Steph waited a few moments before speaking, then uttered, "Mrs. Davis hates me Mom! She hates me because I'm not a normal girl!" Then buried her face in her pillow.

27

Now it was her mother's turn for a moment of silence as she looked heavenward for inspiration. No words came to her mind, instead, she laid on the bed next to her little girl, enveloped her in her arms and allowed her to cry until she fell asleep.

When dinner time came her mother and father knocked on her bedroom door. "Steph, it's time for dinner," they said together. Her tousled hair and flushed cheeks made them smile.

"I'm not hungry," she mumbled.

As they entered the room, she could smell food and looked up to see a tray with some of her favorites. A warm grilled tuna and cheese sandwich, a bowl of pears with cottage cheese and a cold glass of milk. "Are you sure you don't want anything to eat?" Her mother asked, "Remember how your stomach hurts if you skip meals."

"My stomach hurts because of Mrs. Davis!" Steph grumbled, as her father set the tray on the little table next to her bed. "Your mother says you think Mrs. Davis hates you," he noted.

"She does, Dad! She hates me cause I'm a tomboy!" To this, her father encouraged, "Please, tell us everything that happened."

Unable to resist the delicious-smelling food she started to eat, while in between bites explaining her horrible, embarrassing day.

Steph felt better after eating and her father suggested he would like to take her to school a little early the next morning and meet her new teacher. She was very excited about this idea and thought for sure her dad would set Mrs. Davis straight.

The next morning while Steph and her father visited with Mrs. Davis, she instructed them, "If Stephanie wants to wear shorts under her dress to recess, she will need to put them on in the restroom before going out to play and take them off again before coming back to class." Steph wanted to scream at this new rule. She knew it would take half of her recess time!

"Against my better judgment," Mrs. Davis went on, "I can't stop her from playing with the boys, but I warn you Mr. Snell, it is a very dangerous thing for a girl to do." Her father tried to explain how important playing sports was to his daughter, but she would not listen and interrupted him too! Even Steph's father who was a tall, athletic man seemed small standing next to her.

By now the other students were arriving and staring at the three of them, so her father kissed her goodbye whispering, "Kiddo, I love you. We'll talk later when I get home." She hated to see him go and wanted to say, "I'm sick dad, take me with you," but all the kids were standing around and Mrs. Davis had already started snapping her fingers and barking commands.

This day was not much better than the one before. She had been completely wrong about her father setting Mrs. Davis straight and to top it off some of the kids had overheard the conversation and the teasing had begun again. "Remember, you're a girl and it's too dangerous for you to play with the boys at recess." She couldn't wait for the day to be over!

After dinner that night, Steph was playing with Molly in the front room and listened while her father told her mother how *uncompromising* Mrs. Davis had been. She had

29

never heard that word before but was pretty sure it meant *stubborn*. "There's only five weeks of school left," he went on to say, "She'll just have to make the best of it." Steph got a very sick feeling in her stomach again.

Before bed each night, she always went over her spelling words and read with one of her parents. That night it was her father's turn. They had just started a new book called "The Great Brain" and there were parts in it that made them laugh out loud. It was nice to forget about her problems for a while.

As her father tucked her in bed, he comforted her, "You keep doing what makes you feel happy honey. I'm so proud of you. You are the most genuine person I know." Genuine was a new word for Steph so she asked, "What does that mean?"

"It means," her father explained, "That there's nothing fake or phony about you and that is a wonderful thing to be!" He gave her a big hug goodnight and they both said, "I love you" at the same time. She thought about what her father had said and felt a little better inside.

Steph tried her hardest to make things work *and* be respectful toward Mrs. Davis. She took her shorts to school in a small backpack from home and as soon as the recess bell rang, she raced to the girl's bathroom, put on her shorts, then ran as fast as she could out to play ball with the boys. As soon as the bell rang again, Steph would hurry to the bathroom, change back, and get to class. Often, she didn't have time to stand in line at the fountain so she started filling a canteen from home with water so she could have a drink. This went on for two weeks and Steph was getting so tired of it. She knew Mrs. Davis didn't like her and honestly, she didn't like her either.

Then one day, she let her anger get the best of her and did something she should *not* have done!

# Chapter 5

When Mrs. Davis took over for Mrs. Sharp, she filled the windows all along the east wall of the classroom with interesting types of flowers. Some Steph had never heard of before like columbine, kalanchoe and African violets. Mrs. Davis would tell the students all about them and they all knew she *loved* her plants.

One warm spring day, Steph was a few minutes late getting back to class because some fifth-grade girls were inside the bathroom holding the door shut. When they finally rushed out, they laughed at her, saying, "You're going in the wrong bathroom little boy!" Frustrated she growled at them. She had begun to realize that if she let herself get angry, she wouldn't cry and to her being angry seemed better than crying.

Steph kicked the bathroom door and yelled, "I hate school! Nothing here is fair!" Then quickly changed out of her shorts, poked them in her pack and rushed into class with a flushed face.

She started to take out her canteen for a quick sip of water when suddenly she heard Mrs. Davis's all too familiar booming voice, "Miss Snell, why are you late and what are you drinking?" Steph jumped with surprise, spilling some of the water on her face and the floor. She wiped her mouth and tried to explain what had happened, but Mrs. Davis interrupted her, "I knew those shorts would cause a problem! You will need to miss afternoon recess for being late." She wanted to yell at her teacher and argue that she had only been a few minutes late and it wasn't her fault, but she remembered how her father looked trying to reason with her. She plopped into her seat, put her sweaty head down on her desk and mumbled, "OK." Now she felt the tears start to form in the corners of her eyes. She hated school and she hated Mrs. Davis!

When afternoon recess came, all the kids went out to play without her. Mrs. Davis gave her nothing to do, and she also left leaving Steph completely by herself. She sat all alone for a minute, then she couldn't help herself and walked to the big row of windows to watch the kids playing outside. As she stood there, she looked down at the flowerpot in front of her. It was an African violet. Mrs. Davis had told the class what a delicate plant it was and that the leaves and petals bruise very easily. "Even if you brush up against an African Violet it will bruise and turn black." she had informed them. As Steph looked at the flowers lined up along the windowsill, she said out loud, "How would you like it if the principal made you get rid of all these plants you love?"

Suddenly, an idea popped into her mind. She looked around to be sure no one was watching, reached out and pinched every leaf on the African violet. Her heart was pounding so hard and fast she thought it might jump out of her chest. When she felt she had pinched each leaf hard, she quickly sat down at her desk. Shortly after, Mrs. Davis returned. She looked right at Steph, did not say a word, sat down and started correcting papers.

It seemed like forever before the bell rang and the kids began coming back to class. Steph couldn't help sneaking peeks in the direction of the African Violet to see if it had already begun to turn black. It had not. Now she worried she hadn't squeezed hard enough.

Before long, the class became busy learning all about the founder of Kaysville named William Kay and she forgot all about what she had done.

# Chapter 6

The next morning their school day started in the usual way, with the entire class standing, putting their hands on their hearts, and saying "The Pledge of Allegiance" out loud. Steph didn't mind this ritual, but often thought of the last line, Liberty and justice for all? Doesn't that mean fairness and freedom? Mrs. Davis wasn't very fair, and Steph didn't feel very free. As they took their seats after saying the pledge, Steph muttered under her breath, "Liberty and justice for all, as long as you're a normal girl!"

They began their daily work. Arithmetic was always the first thing in the morning. After doing several problems together, Mrs. Davis wrote a few on the chalk board, asked them to copy the problems to their papers and solve them on their own. "Remember," she said sternly, "If there isn't a full name, date and neat handwriting the paper will be thrown away!"

As the class worked quietly, a sudden scream made them jump! "What has happened to my African Violet?" Steph's memory came flooding back and all eyes in the room flashed to the windowsill where Mrs. Davis was bending over the purple-flowered plant with completely black leaves! "Did it get too cold in the school last night?

Was it too close to the window?" she cried. Then the one and only time it ever happened; Mrs. Davis dismissed the students to go outside and have early recess.

Steph watched her teacher carefully holding the pot with the dead-looking plant in it. There was a part of her that felt sorry for what she had done and remembering her promise to her mother, decided she would tell her as soon as she got home.

No one was in the house when Steph walked through the door, but her mother's car was there. She looked out the back window and saw her in the garden. "We always plant after Mother's Day," she proclaimed every May since Steph could remember. She watched as her mother skillfully turned the soil over again and again with the shovel until it was crumbly and loose. Clara Snell was a small but strong woman who wore a hat over her dark brown hair while working in the yard to keep the sun off her face. There were not many things her mother could not do. She was hardworking and always willing to help anybody.

After watching her for a while Steph went outside to keep her promise. "Mom," she quietly called.

"Hi, honey, you're home. How was your day?" her mother questioned, stopping to wipe the sweat off her brow.

"Well, I need to talk to you about that," she answered. Her mother smiled, stopped what she was doing and led her daughter to the shade of their apple tree where Molly was playing with her tinker toys.

Confident her mother would understand, Steph began telling her about Mrs. Davis taking recess away, her wanting to get even by pinching the African Violet leaves and Mrs. Davis's reaction that morning. Her mother listened

36

and when Steph was finally finished, she simply asked, "So, what do you think you could do that would help you and Mrs. Davis feel better?"

Steph thought for a moment then answered, "Well, I have some money in my piggy bank from mowing the lawn, I could give her that?"

"Do you know how much the plant costs?" her mother questioned. Steph admitted she had no idea.

They talked for a while and came up with a plan. Together, they would go to Joe's Greenhouse, their local nursery, and look for an African Violet. She would use her own money to buy it, take the plant to Mrs. Davis and apologize to her. Even though Steph felt Mrs. Davis owed her an apology too, she knew it would probably never happen.

When her father got home, they all went to the greenhouse together. "I need to buy vegetable and flower starts for planting in a week anyway," her mother explained, "We might as well get everything today."

The greenhouse was one of Steph's favorite places to go. It had a wonderful earthy smell, was always warm and the long skinny rows of plastic-covered houses were filled with every color of flower imaginable from the ground to the ceiling.

They found the owner and asked if he had any African Violets. He told them they were a special-order item and kind of expensive. "Will it get here before the end of the school year?" Steph asked.

"If we order it right now, I believe so," he reassured her.

Taking all her mowing money from her jean pocket, Steph placed it on the counter. The man counted all the coins and announced it was only enough for half. But he was kind, and told her, "I'll order it and you can pay the rest when you come to pick it up."

For the next few Saturdays Steph worked hard doing jobs for her parents to earn the rest of the money. She organized the tool shed, helped clean the house, swept off the back patio and cleaned both of their cars inside and out. Finally, they got a phone call from the greenhouse that the African Violet had arrived. They picked it up the day before school got out.

The next morning Steph's dad drove her to school early on his way to the clinic so she wouldn't have to ride on the bus with the plant. "We wouldn't want it to bruise, now would we?" Her dad chuckled and winked at her. She felt nervous even though she knew she was doing the right thing. Mrs. Davis made her feel uptight, and she hoped she wouldn't get angry when Steph told her the truth. Her father could tell how she was feeling and encouraged her, "You're going to be just fine kiddo. I'm very proud of you!"

It looked like she was the only kid in the school as she walked in the front doors. A teacher from the 5$^{th}$ grade stopped her in the hall and asked why she was there so early? Steph was holding the potted plant and explained she had something for her teacher for the end of the school year. The teacher smiled, "Well what a sweet thing to do." Steph nodded and smiled back at her while thinking to herself, "If she only knew the whole story."

When she got to her classroom, she saw Mrs. Davis sitting at her desk writing. Steph softly whispered her name and she looked up over her reading glasses that were halfway down her nose. In that moment Steph noticed she looked very old and kind of sad. "Mrs. Davis," she called out again a little louder this time, "I brought you an African Violet to replace the one that died." She looked surprised and exclaimed, "Miss Snell, what a kind thing for you to do." Steph walked timidly to her desk thinking maybe she should leave it at that. But knew she had to tell the truth, "Well, you see Mrs. Davis, I...I...I was the reason your other one died." She was so nervous her voice was cracking. Finally, she swallowed and was able to continue, "I was mad at you for making me miss recess and thought if I took something away that *you* loved it would make me feel better," she paused, then finally blurted out, "but it didn't!"

Mrs. Davis's lips tightened. Steph could tell she didn't know what to say. The awkward silence made her wish her father had come in with her. After what seemed like forever, Mrs. Davis took off her glasses and sternly stated, "Stephanie, thank you for being honest. You may set it in the window, then go outside and wait for the bell to ring." For just a second her face seemed to soften. Then, she put on her glasses and started to write again.

For that day Mrs. Davis looked a little happier. Perhaps it was because it was the end of the school year? Perhaps it had something to do with her new African Violet? Steph didn't really care which it was, because she had done the right thing and today was the last day she had to have Mrs. Davis as her teacher!

# Chapter 7

Early in the summer of 1968, the Snell family took a vacation to California. Steph was almost nine, Molly was almost four and they were both wildly excited! They went to Sea World, Disneyland, and swam in the ocean for the first time. Yet, Steph's favorite part of the entire trip was the night they went to an Oakland A's baseball game. She loved watching Catfish Hunter strike players out, Rollie Fingers and his crazy mustache and Reggie Jackson hit two home runs. She loved the hot dogs, peanuts, the sounds of everyone cheering and the lights that came on when it started to get dark.

After that game, Steph dreamed of the day when she would be able to wear a uniform and play little league baseball. When they returned home, she practiced in the backyard with Zac and Kenny every afternoon.

On a Saturday morning near the end of June, the tryouts took place. Zac, Kenny, and Steph all showed up with their dads to sign in and get the chance to show off their skills before being placed on a team. They so hoped they would all be on the same one.

As they were standing in line waiting for their turn, a tall, skinny man with a huge Adam's apple walked up to

Steph's father and asked to speak with him in private. At first, she was distracted by the man, thinking he looked like he'd swallowed a golf ball, but then continued to watch the boys out on the field. The closer it came for her turn the more excited she got.

Suddenly, she felt someone tugging her out of the line and looked up to see the same tall man that had been talking with her father earlier. "Come out of the line," he demanded. "You can't play, you're a girl!"

Steph panicked, not wanting to lose her spot. She called out for her father who was now across the field talking with some other men, "Dad, what's going on?" He saw what the man was doing and hustled over to them demanding he let go of his daughter at once. "Dad," Steph repeated, "What's going on?"

Her father took her aside and quietly answered, "Steph, these men are telling me you can't play little league because you're a girl."

The scream was right inside her throat wanting to come out! She was as good as these boys if the coaches would only let her show them, they would see. She pled with the tall man, "Please, mister, just let me try out, I'm good!" But the man walked away shaking his head in disgust.

As she and her father left the baseball diamond, she could feel tears forming in her eyes. "Why Dad, this isn't fair! Boys get to do all the fun stuff." She moaned, "What do I get to do?"

"Kiddo, I'm so sorry." Her father agreed. "It isn't fair! I know how much you were looking forward to this, but for now, you're not going to be able to play."

Steph's heart was breaking, "Dad," she asked with tears running down her cheeks, "What *will* a girl like me ever be able to do?" Her father paused for a moment and she realized, he was trying to hold back his own tears. She couldn't remember ever seeing her father cry. He reached over and pulled her into his chest and held her tightly.

After a few moments, he asked, "Honey, what would you like to do?" Steph wasn't entirely sure what he meant. "Do you mean right now?" she asked. Her father explained his question, "When you are older, what do you want to do then?"

Steph had given a lot of thought to this and responded quickly, "I want to play sports and build things, Dad. Maybe someday I'll even build houses for my job when I'm a grown-up?" Her voice was full of excitement. "And dad I don't want to worry about being teased anymore so I can feel happy and safe!"

Her father held her little chapped hands in his own and looked her in the eyes, "Kiddo," he comforted, "I want you to feel happy and safe too. We'll keep trying together. You keep working hard and learning all you can. I believe someday you *will* be able to do all those things and more."

As they walked toward their car, Steph looked longingly back at the boys playing together, hearing their laughter, and wishing she could be there too.

For the rest of the summer, Steph and her father would go to the baseball diamond before the games started on Saturdays and practice with Zac, Kenny, and some of the other boys on the team. She loved the chance to work out with them and pretended she was playing little league. However, when the umpires came on the field for the *real* games to begin, they made her get off and go sit in the bleachers.

One evening, her father came home with a bucket of old baseballs and a bale of straw. He nailed a big target on it and put it in their backyard. Steph would practice throwing at the target for hours. Her arm got stronger, and her aim got better. She wanted to be ready when someday she would be *free* to play like the boys.

# Chapter 8

One hot August Sunday the weekend before Steph's ninth birthday, all the parents on the street were having their regular after church naps. Steph and the boys were playing in the backyards having a contest who could hit the target on the straw the most times in a row. They were having so much fun when Zac got the brilliant idea of using tomatoes to throw at the target instead of the baseballs!

Most people in their neighborhood had vegetable gardens and August was prime tomato season, so between the three yards, there were plenty of them to throw. Of course, it didn't take long for the game to change and soon they were chucking tomatoes at each other. Now the laughter was riotous and even though Steph had a fleeting thought they might get into trouble; it was swallowed up by the pure pleasure she was having.

Covered from head to toe with red juice and seeds, Zac took his shirt off first, then Kenny, so it seemed only natural for Steph to do the same. She pulled her tomato-soaked t-shirt over her head, threw it on the grass and continue to run through the yards pelting the boys with her accurate arm.

Suddenly, a screech rang out and they all stopped throwing to look in the direction of the cry. There on the

Barrett's back patio, stood Kenny's four-year-old brother holding his face in his hands. Someone had misfired in his direction and hit him in the eye. Within seconds parents began to appear from every household. All three of them were summoned by their full given names and marched to the hoses where they were squirted off by frustrated moms and dads.

As her mother sprayed Steph down, she scolded, "What made you do that? You know we're planning on bottling those tomatoes this week!" Steph could not give her a good answer. Exasperated her mother continued, "Why is your shirt off? You know girls can't take their shirts off like boys!"

Steph, trying not to be sassy, argued, "Why? I look the same as they do mom. I'm not grownup yet!"

This made her mother stop and think. So many things in her little girl's life were not fair. There was no sense making a big deal about the shirt thing today. She turned off the hose and snipped, "Go strip down to your underwear outside the back door and get in the tub!" Steph quickly obeyed as her mother yelled, "And don't forget to wash your hair!"

While in the bathtub she began to worry. It was her birthday in four days, and she had just made her parents mad. She apologized over and over that night, promising to clean up the yard and do whatever they needed help with.

Her parents made her keep the promise. Besides cleaning up smashed tomatoes the next day, she helped pick, scald and bottle 28 quarts of tomatoes as well as cut and core a half bushel of apples to put in their huge dehydrator for dried apple slices.

Steph also didn't complain when it was time for "back to school" shopping, which she hated! Her mother chose a new dress and two new skirts with tops for her to wear in the fourth grade. She wished she could have gotten Levi's and t-shirts like Zac and Kenny but, remembered her promise and thanked her mother for the new outfits.

The night of her ninth birthday, they had all her favorite things to eat. Her dad cooked T-bone steaks on the charcoal grill. Her mom cooked corn on the cob from the garden and steamed a big pot of fresh green beans with lots of melted butter and salt. For dessert, her mother also made fresh peach pies with homemade ice cream and invited Zac and Kenny's families over for birthday pie in the backyard.

Her father placed candles in one of the pies and everyone sang happy birthday to her. As they were eating dessert, Steph's mother brought out two presents. One was a long skinny box with a bow on it and the other was a small flat box with a card. She opened the small gift with the card first.

It read, "I'm sorry I can't be there on your birthday. I Love You, Grandma Snell." Steph's Grandpa Snell had died two years before when she was just seven years old. She didn't remember him very well, but she knew her grandmother, who lived in Salt Lake City, didn't like to drive at night. Steph figured that was why she hadn't come.

Inside the small box were paper dolls and paper doll clothing that had to be cut out. There were little tabs on the tops and the sides of the clothing to fold over the cardboard dolls and hold the clothing in place. Steph scrunched up her nose when she saw what was inside. Her mother quickly gathered up the gift saying, "We'll have to write grandma a thankyou card," knowing full well her daughter would never play with them.

Before her mother had finished putting away the paper dolls, Steph had the long skinny box opened and was screaming, "I can't believe it! I can't believe it!" It was a Daisy lever action bb gun just like the one Zac had gotten for his birthday in June. "Thank you, thank you!" she shouted to her parents. Her father started showing her how to load the bbs in the barrel of the rifle and pump the lever in between each shot, but of course, Steph had shot Zac's so many times she knew all that. The kids all wanted to try shooting that night, but it was getting way too dark, and they still had to clean up dinner dishes.

That night at bedtime, instead of doing their usual reading together, Steph's dad went over the rules of gun safety and reminded her, "We would never have given you a bb gun if we didn't trust you." She thanked him several more times and promised she would always obey the rules. Her father smiled and kissed her goodnight.

She lay awake in bed having a hard time falling asleep. She was so excited to play with her new gift the next day. Over and over again she relived the moment when she opened the box to reveal the rifle. She couldn't imagine anyone thinking that paper dolls were more fun to play with than a bb gun!

# Chapter 9

With only two more days until school started, Steph wasn't going to waste a minute of daylight. She was up when the sun was and out in the backyard. She turned the straw bale into a bb gun target and placed soda cans left from last night's dinner on a piece of two-by-four wood in front of the straw. This way she could shoot at the cans to knock them off the wood and the bbs would go into the straw.

When Zac and Kenny finally came out mid-morning, she had already used all the bbs she had gotten for her birthday and the cans were full of holes. "What are we gonna do now?" Kenny asked disappointedly.

Steph had an idea, "I have some allowance money. Do you guys?"

They each nodded and answered, "A little."

"Well," she ordered, "You guys go get it and your bikes and tell your moms we're going to the drugstore to get more bbs." Then added, "We can get some more sodas too!"

After explaining to her mother and getting permission, Steph jumped on her Schwinn Stingray and met the boys at the corner of their street. She loved her bike, especially the colors. It had a blue body, white fenders, and a red banana seat. Her father called it her "Fourth of July" bike.

It was a beautiful August day and as they rode Steph imagined they were a motorcycle gang going on a big adventure all the way to the Kaysville drug store one mile down the street. When they arrived, they parked their bikes on the sidewalk and ran inside. Zac knew exactly where to find the cardboard rolls of bbs. There were eight left on the shelf. Each tube had 200 bbs and cost 50 cents. That meant they needed $4.00 to buy them all.

They knelt on the floor of the drugstore and emptied out their pockets. Bending over they counted the dollar bills first. Steph had two dollars, Zac pulled out a crumpled one-dollar bill and Kenny also had a one-dollar bill although his was neatly folded in half. Then they counted their coins. Steph had a bunch of change because she had helped her parents clean out their cars and got the keep all the money she found. She had an additional $1.27, and Zac had four quarters. They did the math and had a total of $6.27.

Excitedly, they grabbed all eight rolls of bbs and headed to the soda isle. They all liked orange Fanta, but it wasn't on sale. RC Cola was the best deal. It was 4 cans for $1.00. "I don't even like RC Cola!" Zac grumbled.

"I don't either," Steph declared, "but we can get eight cans to shoot if we buy it instead of orange Fanta!" This made sense, so they grabbed eight cans and headed to the cashier.

Steph recognized the lady at the checkout counter as a friend of her parents. The lady remembered her too and greeted them with a smile, "Looks like you're going to have some fun!"

They all nodded excitedly, as Steph announced, "Yep, I got a bb gun for my birthday yesterday and we ran out of bbs." The lady exclaimed, "Well Stephanie Snell, after God made you, He broke the mold didn't He!" Steph nodded, dumped the money on the counter and asked for three bags so they could split up the goodies and each have something to carry.

They told the lady thanks, hopped back on their bikes and headed home. Riding along with her bag of bbs and soda clanking on her gooseneck handlebars, Steph couldn't help thinking about what the checkout lady had said. *Why would God make only one tomboy in the world?* She wondered. She had learned in school that no two people have the exact same fingerprints, but this was different. She had wished more than anything else to find another girl just like her to be friends with and if the checkout lady was right, that meant…

"Steph where are you going?" She heard someone yelling. "Why didn't you turn?" It was Kenny. She had been so deep in thought she missed their street.

"Oh!" She chuckled. "I was just thinking about stuff."

When they got back to their yards, they opened all the RC colas and dumped them in the garden. They laughed as some of the cans sprayed all over them from the bike ride home and watched as the bubbly brown liquid soaked into the dirt. They set the empty cans on the wood and loaded the bbs guns.

The afternoon was full of fun and they used up seven of the eight rolls of bbs by the time they heard the calls to come in for dinner. The three of them said good night and Steph headed in to wash up. She hated to see the summer end. The beginning of another school year meant dresses every day and maybe another teacher like Mrs. Davis.

# Chapter 10

Steph barged through the back door yelling, "My teacher is a man, and he is awesome!"

Her mother smiled inquiring, "What makes him so awesome?"

Steph grinned. "He's funny, he's fair, and good at sports! He even comes outside with us at recess. He played basketball in college and can make a shot from anywhere on the blacktop!" Steph took a breath. "And, he lets me play too!" Her mother agreed wholeheartedly, this was indeed a good reason for her to feel her teacher was wonderful. Her fourth-grade year was off to a great start thanks to her first male teacher Mr. Sanders.

Another wonderful thing that happened shortly after school started was her parents announced they were having another baby. Steph was thrilled! She had noticed her mother hadn't been cooking as much. A couple times each week her father would bring home fish and chips from the Dairy Queen for dinner and her mother rarely ate hers. Now it made sense!

To help, Steph learned how to make grilled cheese sandwiches with Campbell's tomato soup so that on nights when her father was late getting home it was her responsibility to get dinner for herself and Molly. This made her feel grown-up and in charge.

One night Steph's father came home with a thing called an IV. It was a bag of water with a long skinny tube. "Your mother is dehydrated, and this will help her feel better," he told her. Steph worried, she had helped her mother peel and slice apples to put in their big food dehydrator and remembered how juicy the apple slices were when they went in and how shriveled up and dried they were when they came out.

Later after dinner, Steph asked her father, "So does Mom look like a dried apple slice?"

Her father smiled, "No kiddo, when a person is dehydrated it means they need more fluid in them. Your mother doesn't feel like drinking, so this is like giving her a drink in her arm." He motioned for her to come with him and see her mother.

As she went into her parent's bedroom, she was a little nervous about what she might find. Her mother was laying down on the bed with the tube stuck in her left arm and the bag of water hanging on a hook above her. She was happy to see that her mother looked normal and not like a dried apple slice.

A big smile came over her mother's face as she called for Steph to come lay beside her. "There's my girl. Bless your heart, you have been such a big help." Steph beamed. She loved it when her mother told her, "Bless your heart." She went on, "I want to tell you some exciting news." Steph already knew about the baby so wondered what other exciting news there could be? "Your father and I have decided to make our home a little bigger," she declared,

"We are going to turn the whole back deck into part of our house!"

Her mother continued to explain how the remodeling would create another bedroom for the baby and a larger family room and dining room area for all of them to gather. Steph was excited but mostly loved lying next to her mother. She had missed spending time with her the past few weeks.

About a week later Steph came home from school to find workers in her back yard tearing off all the wood handrails and slats from their old deck and piling them next to the house. She was so excited to see all that wood and ran in the house yelling, "Mom, Mom, can I have all that wood from off the deck?" Her mother was sitting up on the living room sofa sipping a lime rickey. It seemed to be the only thing that sounded good to her these days.

She laughed. "You would like that wouldn't you?" And signaled for Steph to come to sit by her. "What would you do with it?" She inquired.

"I would build things, Mom! I could build a fort and benches to sit on, bird feeders and all kinds of things!" Her mind was full of ideas for the wood. "Let's talk to Dad when he gets home and see what he thinks."

Her mother replied. "Now lets' run through your spelling words before you go out to play."

Steph knew her father would let her keep the wood. Every day after school she raced home, changed out of her dress, and headed out to the wood pile. Zac and Kenny couldn't play as much these days. They were busy with little league football. Steph didn't even ask this time. She knew if the tall man that looked like he'd swallowed a golf ball wouldn't let girls play baseball, he certainly wouldn't let them play football.

She spent hours each day after school using the hammer to pull out the nails and pound them as straight as she could. Some of them broke but most of them she could salvage.

After several weeks she had a big pile of wood with no nails and a bucket of old nails to build with. Her first project was going to be a fort. She had drawn out the plan on paper before starting. It would be four feet tall and four feet by four feet across. The wood slats from the old deck were mostly four feet in length already, so Steph figured that meant less sawing for her. It would have a top deck area with a handrail all along the edge for safety so Molly could play on it too, and a ladder at one end to climb up. Underneath would be a hideout with a door and a window. She worked day after day sawing and hammering. In the beginning, Steph's hands were sore but after a while, they formed callouses and got stronger.

Now the days were getting shorter as well as cooler and Steph often ran out of daylight. Kenny and Zac would bring their hammers and help when they could and soon the fort was completed. Steph wanted to build a couple of benches for the top of the fort next but was almost out of nails. Her father took her to Kaysville Building supply one Saturday and bought her five pounds of new nails and a brand-new hand saw. She was so excited. The nails pounded into the wood so much easier and the saw she had been using was very old. This new saw cut through the wood much faster.

The fort was on the east side of the patio away from the basketball court and right under an apple tree. Sometimes, her mother would bring snacks to the three of them in little plastic baskets and they would eat on top of the fort in the shade of the tree.

One afternoon, Steph and her buddies were playing on the fort when Zac spotted some huge apples high up in the tree. "One of those apples sure sounds good right now." He drooled. They all agreed, so Steph climbed from the top of the fort onto some limbs to reach the apples and toss them down. As she did so, she caught sight of a beautiful round paper wasp nest. It was the size of a basketball!

At first, she was nervous not wanting to get stung but, could see no wasps buzzing around. She figured it must be empty. "This is just the kind of thing Mr. Sanders would love!" she shouted.

Kenny ran to get his father's pruning shears and Steph carefully cut off the small branch without disturbing the nest. They placed it in a large brown paper bag, then sat on the top of the fort, eating the delicious apples, and imagining Mr. Sander's excitement when they brought it for show and tell the next day.

Before they knew it, the sun had gone down, it was getting cold and time to say goodnight. Steph placed the paper bag by the back door so she wouldn't forget to grab it on her way to the bus the next morning.

"Steph, wake up, we overslept!" her mother shouted from the doorway. Her father had an emergency during the night at the hospital and wasn't home yet. "Hurry," her mother muttered, "You'll miss the bus!"

Steph put on a dress and her shorts then ran downstairs for breakfast. Her mother had made hard-boiled eggs with toast and orange juice, some of her favorites. She was glad her mom was feeling better now because she was tired of eating shredded wheat.

"Don't forget to wear a jacket, it's chilly out there." Her mother reminded. She found her favorite gray sweatshirt from her closet, kissed her mother and Molly goodbye and ran out the back door grabbing the bag with the wasp nest. It was going to be a great day.

The morning was crisp, and Steph was thankful for the sweatshirt. Kenny and Zac showed up and they all kept peeking inside the bag as they waited for the bus. It finally arrived, and they all jumped on, heading to their usual seats near the back. Dusty, the bus driver, had the heater on that morning and the bus felt warm after standing in the cool morning air. Steph sat down and was thankful to feel the warmth blowing on her bare legs.

Dusty was an older man that wore overalls every day of his life. He got the nickname Dusty from his gray hair, although he had very little of it anymore. He sometimes wasn't very patient with the more energetic kids like Steph. Because of this, they often called him Crusty Dusty behind his back.

As they bumped along picking up more children, Steph noticed there were some flies on the bus. She thought it was odd because all the windows were up. Stop after stop she saw more and more flies.

Suddenly a girl with long blonde hair sitting in the front stood up and started slapping her head while screaming, "It's stinging me, it's stinging me!" Steph looked down at the brown paper bag sitting by the heater and gasped. The wasp nest was not empty and now in the warmth of the bus, the wasps were waking up and buzzing all over. Kids were screaming and crying. Crusty Dusty was yelling for the kids to sit down and shut up. At that moment she knew what she must do. She grabbed the bag and ran to the front of the bus. "Dusty open the door!" she shouted. At first, he looked at her angrily and almost told her to get back to her seat, but then he saw and heard the paper bag. Quickly, he pulled the bus over in front of the Kaysville City Library and swung the folding door open. As Steph flung the sack onto the street he bellowed, "What the heck was that?"

"That was going to be the best show and tell ever," she lamented.

The library was only one block away from the elementary school and Dusty ordered everyone off. As soon as the bus was empty, he went around opening all the windows to let out the wasps. The kids walked excitedly the rest of the way to the school as Steph trudged slowly behind wondering how much trouble she would get into this time. Zac and Kenny were laughing and talking about it with all the other kids.

Mr. White, the principal, saw the procession of children coming to school on foot and came out the front doors asking them if the bus had broken down? They were all pointing in Steph's direction and telling him what had happened.

All morning long she expected a call over the loudspeaker requesting her to report to the office. But it never came.

Then just before morning recess, Mr. Sanders asked for the class to come to attention. "Before recess, I wanted to give you an update concerning our unfortunate mishap on the bus this morning." Steph squirmed in her seat as he went on, "Luckily, only one little girl got stung and the bus driver was able to clear out the bus for the ride home after school." A bunch of kids cheered. "However," he declared, "Because of what happened a new rule has been made by our principal. Nothing alive can be brought for show and tell anymore!" A few "boos" were heard after the new rule was announced, but Mr. Sanders put an end to that.

Steph wanted to stand and explain that she hadn't thought it *was* alive but kept her mouth shut. Some of the kids were mad for a while. They had cats and dogs they wanted to bring. But for the most, the event was forgotten, yet occasionally, Steph would be walking down the hall or out at recess and hear buzzzzzzzing followed by laughter.

# Chapter 11

When the weather started to get cold and the playground was covered with snow, Mr. Sanders announced he was starting a basketball league during afternoon recesses in the lunchroom. Steph felt anxious and wasn't sure what to think. She decided to be the last person outside to recess and hung back to talk to Mr. Sanders.

She found him in the teacher's supply room. "Mr. Sanders?" she began, standing in the doorway. She knew it was against the rules for students to go in. "Mr. Sanders? Can I play too?" He turned now to face her, pushing his dark-rimmed glasses back up his nose and announced, "Of course." Steph couldn't believe her ears and clarified, "So I can play in the basketball league with the boys?" Mr. Sanders stopped what he was doing, looked right at her and while nodding emphasized, "Yes, Stephanie, you can play!" "Thank you, Mr. Sanders, Thank you!" She gushed and ran outside in the cold winter air having forgotten her coat.

She found Zac and Kenny playing basketball on one of the two courts that had no snow and shouted, "Mr. Sanders says I can play too!" They both looked at her funny as she went on, "So, do you want to get a team together with me? We'll need two more players."

"Sure," they replied and threw her the ball. Steph realized she had worried for no reason. The boys were used to her playing with them now and there had been no question in their minds. Still, she thought, it would sure be nice if there was at least one other girl that wanted to play.

The three of them formed a team with two boys from the fifth grade. Of course, she was the only girl and some of the boys on the other teams had to tease her and her teammates about having a "sissy" on the team. But the teasing didn't last long. They quickly realized Steph was no sissy and their team was unbeatable.

Twice each week at afternoon recess, they would play against another team of boys while Mr. Sanders would referee. Steph loved *game days* and got very excited for them.

She asked Santa for a new pair of shoes like the boys had so she could run faster and jump higher. When Christmas morning came, she was delighted to find that Santa had indeed left her a new pair of white converse high-top sneakers that fit her perfectly.

Most of the boys accepted Steph as one of the guys and seemed to like her. Sometimes though, the fifth-grade boys on her team would talk about girls who were cute and dreamy. She learned the difference between the boys liking her and the boys *liking* other girls. In fact, on Valentine's Day a boy from her team named Barry showed her some chocolates in a little heart box he bought for his girlfriend Sally. She was a typical girl with long dark hair, who wore pretty dresses and black satin shoes. Her knees and elbows were never scraped and scabby like Steph's were, and she had no idea what to do if a basketball came her way. Steph was pretty sure the boys would *never* like her the way Barry liked Sally or ever think she was cute? She tried not to worry about it and for the time being, was satisfied they let her play.

Fourth grade was going by so fast, and Steph knew it was mostly because of Mr. Sanders. He didn't tolerate any "bullying" as he called it and if he heard of it happening there was trouble! Her life at home was also going well, especially now that the remodeling was completed. Their house had been such a mess, but the workers had finished by the middle of February and their home seemed much bigger than before. Her mother's tummy was also getting bigger, and Steph was excited the baby would be coming around Mother's Day. She wondered if she would get a little brother or another little sister?

One night while Steph's family was sitting around the dinner table, her parents announced they would like her to try piano lessons. "You're old enough now and getting to be such a good reader," her mother emphasized, "It's a perfect time for you to start!"

Steph *hated* the idea of taking piano lessons! Why did her parents have to upset her life when it was just starting to get better? She didn't want to be a piano player. It sounded so boring. Her mother saw her long face and tried to be upbeat, "I think you'll be excited to know that Zac and his older sister Karen are also taking lessons. You can all go together to Mrs. Tanner's house and play while you wait for each other to finish." This made Steph a little less unhappy to think her buddy Zac would have to do it too.

Mrs. Tanner was her mother's friend and she had five sons. The older two boys went to the same school as Steph,

61

and she had played football and basketball with them at recess. She had also gone to their house several times with her mother and played in their big backyard that had a basketball court, a jungle gym, and a new thing called a trampoline.

At bedtime when her mother came to read with her, Steph grumbled about taking lessons again. "It's important that you get some background in music." Her mother snapped back, not as patient as usual. "Everyone needs to learn to play an instrument!"

Steph argued, "I will play an instrument Mom, just not the piano." Her mother looked at her tiredly and asked, "Well, what instrument do you want to play?" She had already thought about this and blurted out, "The bagpipes!" Her mother began laughing and Steph couldn't help giggling too. "Well, that's wonderful dear," she said between chuckles, "You can play the bagpipes someday, but you'll need to learn how to read music first, so you're going to start with the piano, and that's that!" Steph knew not to push anymore.

It was tough for her to sit on the hardwood bench next to her teacher and focus on the little black dots that looked like Chinese writing to her. She hated practicing at home too. Her mother insisted on sitting next to her and making Steph count out loud, correcting her frequently. "How could piano be a good thing when it causes us to fight?" She bawled. "We never had fights before piano lessons!"

After school one day, her mother surprised her with a box about the size of a football. She held it. It was too heavy to be a football. "Open it," her mother smiled, "I think this will help both of us." She tore it open to find a curious triangular wood box about ten inches tall that looked like a clock. "It's called a metronome," her mother reported, "It will help you keep time when you practice the piano!" Steph didn't know what to say. "Now hurry, change your clothes and I'll show you how to use it."

Learning to set the metronome was easy and keeping time to the click, click, click *was* better than her mother sitting next to her counting in her ear. Yet it was still hard for Steph to learn the songs. Often, she got discouraged. Seldom did she feel she was getting better.

One Sunday night, something happened that helped her to change her attitude. A young woman in her early twenties came to visit her father at the house. She had just graduated from the University of Utah and was going on to medical school to become a doctor. Her purpose in coming was to ask Dr. Snell some questions about going to medical school. Steph suddenly perked up and put her sketching pad aside thinking, "Wow, I've never heard of a girl doctor before. That's so cool!" While the girl visited with her parents, Steph listened. She recounted how difficult school had been for her when she was younger. Her parents had helped her constantly especially with reading and spelling. She had to develop study habits and continually work at getting good grades all through high school and college.

Steph thought about her own difficult time learning to read. Both her parents, but especially her mother, had worked with her every day helping her to sound out words, spell them and remember what they meant. She remembered the dreaded timed SRAs (Silent Reading Assessments) in second and third grade. They were large cards with stories written on both sides and five questions

63

at the end. The students were given three minutes to read both sides and comprehend what they had read so they could answer the questions. She felt defeated when the timer would buzz, and she hadn't even turned the card over. *Why am I so slow?* She thought to herself.

Feeling there was no hope for her, she started turning the card over, even though she wasn't finished, just so the other kids thought she was reading as fast as they were. Then she would have to guess at the questions having no idea what the answers were.

When her parents saw her scores, her mother arranged to bring some of the SRA cards home for them to practice with and in time, and with much effort, Steph got better. She wished reading, spelling and arithmetic could have been as natural and easy to her as throwing and catching a ball.

Thinking that piano might be the same as school, she made up her mind to do better. "I'm going to do everything Mrs. Tanner tells me to do and stop arguing with my mother!" She promised herself in the bathroom mirror while brushing her teeth that night. And she kept her promise.

In the weeks that followed, the notes began to make more sense to her, and she felt herself improve. Best of all, she and her mother stopped fighting. Steph practiced her spring recital piece "Rain, Rain Go Away" so many times that even Molly screamed, "Mom, make her stop!" But it paid off because at the recital she played her number perfectly!

On a Tuesday near the end of the school year, Steph had just finished her piano lesson and was headed to the backyard when she looked out the window to see a new kid with long hair playing ball with the boys. "Is that a girl?"

She quizzed Mrs. Tanner. "Her name is Janet Barton," she answered, "and her family just moved into the house next door. You need to meet her Stephanie, you girls are a lot alike."

Janet had freckles and shoulder-length strawberry blonde hair cut in a shag style and parted up the middle. She was the same size as Steph, and they became quick friends. They played basketball against the boys and beat them two out of three times. She learned that Janet had a twin brother, a dog named Tiger, a stingray bike with a banana seat *and* she was a *tomboy* too!

That day Steph floated home from piano lessons bouncing up the back steps and through the door, "Mom, the best thing happened at piano today!" She burst into the kitchen. This surprised her mother because her daughter never came home excited from piano lessons. Steph continued, "I made a new friend named Janet at Mrs. Tanner's house, and guess what Mom, she's *just like me!* In fact, Mrs. Tanner says we're like *two peas in a pod*!" She looked straight at her mother and cheered, "You were right mom, there is another tomboy in the world!" Her mother smiled and gave her a big hug. "Come on." She motioned for her to follow. "Tell me all about your new friend."

# Chapter 12

The next morning, Steph was up before her parents were, too excited to sleep. "Mom!" She entered their room. "Mom, is it time for school yet?" Her father and mother both looked up surprised to see her standing there. "It's only six in the morning." Her mother mumbled. By this time, her belly was very large, and it was hard for her to sit up in bed. Seeing his wife struggle, Steph's father insisted, "You lie back down sweetheart, I'll make some pancakes and eggs for all of us." Her mother didn't argue and plopped back down on the bed.

She and her father made a batch of pancakes and there was plenty of time for her to create animal shapes on the grill. While they were cooking her father asked, "So you pretty excited to have your new friend Janet at school, kiddo?"

"Yes, Dad!" She smiled, "It'll be so nice to have another girl who likes to play sports. The boys are going to flip!" "Well, you'll have to invite her over to play," her father exclaimed, "Mom and I can't wait to meet her!"

Gulping down her pancakes, she hurriedly brushed her teeth, dressed for school, and sat in front of the living room window that looked out over the street. At last, she started to see other kids heading for the bus stop and yelled, "See ya!" to her family as she skipped out the door.

When she arrived at school, she jumped off the bus and scanned the backfield looking for Janet who lived close enough to ride her bike with her twin brother Joey. Joey was in the same class as Steph, but Janet was in Mrs. Johnson's class right next to hers. She wished it could be the other way around.

Finally, she spotted them, "Janet!" she yelled, "Come on, I'll show you around." She took her on a tour of the classrooms, the lunchroom, the bathrooms, where to get drinks and where to meet her at recess. "I can't believe you get to play football with the boys." Janet smiled. "At my last school there was NO WAY I got to play," Steph told Janet all about Mrs. Sharp, Mr. Sanders and wearing shorts under her dresses every day. Just when she was going to tell her all about Mrs. Davis, the bell rang signaling the beginning of school.

The morning dragged by. Steph glanced at the clock at least a hundred times before finally, the first recess bell rang. She met Janet by the outside drinking fountain, and they headed to the field. Ronnie frowned as he watched the two girls approach but, he didn't say a word. He knew Steph would go straight to Mr. Sanders if he tried to stop them from playing. Some of the other boys also gave awkward glances but then shrugged their shoulders and laughed that there was another girl who wanted to play with them. Zac and Kenny were fine with the girls being on their team and as the game began it became obvious who was going to win. Their team scored so many touchdowns, they all stopped counting. Janet was even faster than Steph and outran the boys every time she got the ball.

As the bell sounded ending recess, Janet cheered, "That was so much fun! I love this school!" Steph agreed, "Yep, those little league coaches are so stupid not to let us play!" And they laughed running arm in arm into the school.

# Chapter 13

It didn't take long for Janet and Steph to become inseparable and regulars in each other's homes. Besides her twin brother, Janet had a little sister named Marnie who was about the same age as Molly. Her parents were very nice and funny. Janet's mom made up a new nickname for Steph calling her Stephinitis. Whenever she would walk into their house Mrs. Barton would say, *"Hello, Stephinitis, at ease disease, there's fungus among us."* And the girls would roll their eyes and laugh.

Mr. Barton traveled a lot with his work but when he was there, he let the girls ride their two little Harley Davidson minibikes. This was very exciting for Steph as she knew her father would never buy a motorcycle of any kind. In fact, he called them *murdercycles* because as a doctor, he had seen so many accidents on them. When they played at the Snell's home, they did things with Zac and Kenny too. Most afternoons were filled with playing two on two basketball, shooting bb guns, playing on the fort, or riding minibikes all around the neighborhood.

One Saturday morning, Steph's parents asked all the kids to help get the garden ready for planting. "You know we always plant after Mother's Day," her mother reminded,

"But this year I don't know how much I'll be able to do with the baby coming." The four buddies were happy to help and worked hard digging and raking the garden plot. By one o'clock in the afternoon, it was all tilled and looked beautiful. Everyone was tired and hungry so Steph's dad announced, "Let's all go to the Dairy Queen for lunch, and you can order whatever you want!" They eagerly piled into the back of the Snell's station wagon for the short ride downtown. Four bacon cheeseburgers with fries and milkshakes later they were full and couldn't move. They all went back to Steph's house and played Parcheesi until it was time for everyone to go home.

That night, her parents thanked her for being such a hard worker and helping with her friends. "You seem so much happier," her mother said. "I am, Mom," Steph responded, "I have a best friend now!" Her parents smiled. They knew it was also a wonderful teacher who had helped make such a positive change in their little girl. It seemed amazing to them the difference just one or two people can make in another person's life.

The next morning was Mother's Day and Mrs. Barrett was in the Snell's kitchen making scrambled eggs with toast when Steph woke up. "What's going on?" she asked sleepily.

"Your parents went to the hospital during the night!" Mrs. Barrett smiled. "Your mother is having the baby!" Steph excitedly ran back upstairs to wake up Molly. "Mom's having the baby today!" She ran into her little sister's room.

They had just started eating when the telephone rang. It was their dad telling them they had a little baby brother!

Molly and Steph hugged each other. "Yes!" they cheered, "We can't wait to come see him!"

After breakfast, the Snell girls made some Mother's Day cards then went to church with Kenny's family. When they got back, their dad was there, changing his clothes. They were so glad he was home and anxious to go to the hospital to see their mother and new baby brother.

First, they visited their mom for a few minutes and gave her the cards they had made. She seemed very tired and had a hard time staying awake while they were talking. "I think we should let your mother sleep for a while," their father whispered, watching his wife dose off. "Let's go see the baby shall we!"

George Snell and his girls walked happily down the hall to the big glass windows of the nursery. About a dozen babies were in little boxes on wheels all lined up so people could see them. Only the nurses and doctors could go in, so they watched through the window. Steph saw the name Snell on one of the boxes and the nurse rolled it over so they could see the baby up close. The little bundled body was so tiny that Molly cried out, "He's like my dolly!" Which made them smile.

Their father proudly announced, "We have decided to name him Steven."

The girls cheered and Steph added, "Of course we'll call him Steve!" All three of them giggled until the nurses came out into the hall and shushed them.

For the next few days, Steph got to stay at Janet's house after school and Molly went with one of her friends during the days until their mother got home from the hospital. It was fun to be with Janet's family, but she couldn't wait to have her mother and new baby brother home.

Steven was so cute but loud. Steph didn't remember Molly crying as much as he did but loved when it was her turn to feed him. She learned how to warm up the bottle in a pan of water on the stove, check the formula on the inside of her wrist to make sure it wasn't too hot and put the burp cloth under his chin before feeding him. This process took a while and Steve was not very patient. He would cry and cry waiting to be fed, yet the instant the bottle was stuck in his mouth he started sucking and stopped crying. She was good at checking to see how many ounces he drank. "Every two ounces you need to burp him," her mother instructed. When she would take the bottle out and sit him up, Steve would cry and cry again until he finally let out a loud burp of gas.

One day while Steph was feeding him, he started grunting and his face turned deep red. She worried for a second then suddenly heard and felt a rush of poop come out of him. She looked down and saw the mess coming out of the cloth diaper around his little legs. "Mom," she cried out, "Steven just pooped all over me!" Her mother came into the room and saw what had happened. They both started to laugh. "Well," her mother giggled, "That's what having kids is all about, lots of fun and lots of messes!"

# Chapter 14

Memorial Day was quickly approaching and so was the end of fourth grade. Steph had such mixed emotions about this. Of course, she looked forward to summer as always, but she had already begun the ***what-if*** worry game.

What if the two women teachers in fifth grade wouldn't let her wear shorts under her dresses each day?

What if they wouldn't let the girls play sports with the boys?

What if they didn't like tomboys?

And the worst what if of all was, *what if* they are just like Mrs. Davis?

Janet and Steph often played the what-if game, but Janet was better at changing the subject and thinking of more fun things to do with their time.

The girls decided they wanted to do something nice for Mr. Sanders. Steph's mother suggested they make something for him and write a nice thankyou note thanking him for all he had done. These ideas sounded great, and they got to work. There was still some of the wood left from the remodeling, so they decided to build a planter box and put some beautiful flowers in it for his porch. They had so much fun building and painting it together and even used their own money to buy petunias from the greenhouse to plant inside. They also used their very best cursive handwriting to write notes to him.

When they took the gifts to Mr. Sanders on the last day of school, he was very touched and thanked them sincerely. He was surprised they had built the beautiful planter by themselves.

"I want to tell you some exciting news." He smiled, having them sit down, "Some of the parents in our community recognize the need for a summer program to help boys *and girls* stay active during the months when they are not in school." Their faces brightened as he went on, "We are going to hold this program at the high school every Tuesday and Thursday each week and play games together like tennis, kickball, softball and track events. I know I can plan on you two being there!"

Steph and Janet reassured him they were thrilled about it, but wondered if they would be the only girls? Mr. Sanders explained, "We are opening this up to all of Davis County so anyone, boys or girls ages 8-11 can come. I certainly hope you are not the only two girls!"

The first day of the summer program arrived and Steph had butterflies in her stomach she was so eager to see who showed up! Her father dropped her off a little early with her bike so she could ride home after they were finished. "Good luck kiddo!" He grinned. "Have so much fun playing ball." Steph waved and told him she would. Not too many kids were there yet so she rode her bike toward Janet's house, but Janet was also coming early.

"I couldn't wait!" She giggled as they almost ran into each other coming around the corner.

They waited and watched every car and bicycle as they arrived. Most of the kids were boys, but some were girls! Some had short hair like Steph's, and some had long hair like Janet's, but all of them came ready to have the chance to play!

Once all the boys and girls arrived, there was a short meeting to introduce the coaches and go over the rules. Mr. Sanders was one of the head coaches and did most of the talking. Steph wondered if she would see the tall, skinny coach that wouldn't let her play little league the summer before, but thankfully he was nowhere in sight.

The coaches split everyone into squads with both girls and boys in each group. Janet and Steph were not together but every team had two or three girls, and most of the girls were good! She had so much fun meeting girls from Layton, Clearfield, Farmington, and many other surrounding towns. All of them told similar stories of wishing they could play sports but hearing the words, *"You can't play, you're a girl!"* For some reason it made her feel better she hadn't been the only one.

When the first day ended, Steph was so excited to tell her mother about her morning that she told Janet she would call her later and quickly rode her bike home. She found her mom feeding Steven on the sofa as she burst through the door. "Mom," she exclaimed, "you won't believe how many other tomboys there are in the world!" Her mother grinned. She had often worried about her little girl's happiness and it was such a relief to see her enthusiastic about life.

# Chapter 15

One Tuesday when Steph arrived home from the summer games, she found her mother's sister at her house visiting with her son, Larry. Steph and Larry were the same age and even though she didn't see him much, they enjoyed playing together although they often got into trouble. While the sisters were chatting happily and making lunch, the two kids went downstairs to the playroom. Unknown to Steph, her cousin had developed a curiosity about matches.

"Hey," he whispered once they were away from their mothers, "Wanna light some matches?"

Steph cautioned, "I don't know if that's a good idea. Besides, I don't know where my parents keep them."

"I have some," he announced, "Come on, let's have a contest!"

Steph's parents had bought her a large "A" framed easel a few years before for her to paint on. It had a roll of white butcher paper at the top and a tray to hold paints near the bottom. Larry pulled a fresh sheet of paper down to the tray, took a book of matches out of his pocket and lit the bottom of the roll. Steph watched as the flame took hold and slowly turned the paper black as it crept higher and higher.

*Slap!* Larry's hand hit the paper against the wood easel putting the flame out. "Your turn!" he ordered, handing her the matches. Steph was nervous but also curious. She had never lit a match before. Unfolding the cover, it revealed the paper sticks with red tips that looked like tiny soldiers all lined up in neat little rows. Her hands trembled as she tore one off and struck it against the scratch strip.

Nothing happened.

Again.

Nothing.

Finally, on the third attempt the end of the stick jumped into flame. She held it under the paper until the fire took. Watching in fascination she burned her fingers a little forgetting to put the match out. As with Larry's, the flame crept up the white paper turning the remains behind it black. She could smell the smoke and knew her mother would know what they were doing. She quickly slapped it out and grunted, "This is stupid. Let's go outside and play!"

Thankfully, Larry went along as she headed out the basement door to the fort. However, within minutes they heard their mothers yelling, "Have you two been lighting matches? We can smell smoke!"

They didn't answer and looked at each other wondering what they should say. Then Steph saw her mother coming up the basement steps with her scrub bucket in her hand.

Fuming, she yelled, "Stephanie Snell and Larry Wilson you get in here this instant!"

The cousins hopped off the fort and briskly walked to where her mother was standing. "Do you two know how lucky you are you didn't burn the house down?" Her mother was madder than Steph had ever seen her. "You both have a huge mess to clean up!"

As they walked into the playroom, they were shocked. The entire roll of butcher paper was black. "We thought we put it out!" Steph screamed, "I'm so sorry mom! I should have told Larry no!" The wet burned paper was everywhere from her mother throwing the pail of water to put out the flames.

"Get started," she growled handing them each some rags and a bucket, "And don't stop until this playroom is spic and span!"

They didn't say a word to each other. Steph was so mad at herself and her cousin. It seemed that every time Larry came to play, she got into trouble.

At bedtime, her parents both came to her room and informed her of her punishment. She was grounded for the rest of the week from any friends including the summer sports program. Steph cried and cried but knew deep down inside she deserved it. She had done a stupid thing that could have turned out very bad.

The next morning, she had to call Janet and tell her what had happened. In the afternoon when Kenny and Zac came over to play, she had to tell them the story all over again. "I can't do anything with friends until Monday." She mumbled. It was the longest four days of her life.

The rest of the summer flew by and Steph realized how much she appreciated Janet's friendship more each day. Not only did they understand each other but they always had lots of fun together and *never* came up with ideas that got them into trouble.

On the last day of the summer sports program, the coaches held a huge competition at the high school track. Boys and girls competed together in the same events. The only separations were by age. Steph competed in all the age nine to ten-year-old races and field events winning many awards. She felt like an Olympian as she arrived home with all the medals around her neck. "Wow," her mother exclaimed, "You're amazing! Did Janet win some awards too?"

"Oh yes," Steph bragged, "She won lots and so did the other girls. I have no idea why those little league coaches don't want any girls on their team, cause we're good!" This brought a delightful smile to her mother's lips.

The end of summer was always a sad time for Steph. The only thing to look forward to now was her 10th birthday. "So, what do you want for your birthday?" her parents quizzed one night at dinner. She had been so busy during the summer she hadn't given it much thought.

"Hmmmmm, let me think? Maybe my own minibike?" She teased.

Her father murmured, "I will never buy my children a *murdercycle*!"

Steph laughed. "I knew you would say that!"

"I do have an idea though," her father suggested. "Mr. Barnes, Mr. Barrett and I have been talking about a camping trip with you and the boys to a place in Wyoming called Shoshone Lake."

"Really?" Steph perked up. "Can Janet come too?" She asked.

"I think that could be arranged," he replied, "but there's lots to do to get ready because we leave in three days!"

Janet's parents agreed to let her come and everyone worked hard to get things ready for the big trip. They packed food, water, snacks, tents, sleeping bags and three canoes. The more they packed the more excited they all became!

# Chapter 16

Janet slept over the night before they left because the dads wanted to leave at 5:00 in the morning. It was dark and a little chilly when Steph's dad came to wake them up. The kids all rode in the back of her station wagon, while Mr. Barnes and Mr. Barrett drove the truck and trailer with all the canoes and their gear.

Her father had made a bed so they could all lay down and hopefully sleep. They napped for a while but as soon as the sun was up, so were they. They played the alphabet game and Steph's dad quizzed them on the different makes and models of cars as they passed by, but it still seemed like forever before they finally turned onto a dirt road that headed toward a huge pine forest.

After several miles of bumping around on the dusty road, they arrived at the parking lot and started to unload. They had to put all their gear into the canoes and paddle everything to their campground because no vehicles were allowed into the camps nor any motorized boats on Shoshone Lake.

They all took turns paddling across the beautiful crystal, clear water. It was so clean they could see the fish swimming beneath them. The lake was surrounded by huge lodgepole pines on every side, and they were the only people around. Steph had never seen anything so beautiful or smelled anything more wonderful than this place. She continually took deep breaths wishing her backyard could smell this good.

It took them almost an hour to paddle across the lake to their camp which was a few hundred feet from the shore. They quickly began to unload the canoes and started setting up their tents. The dads slept in one, Zac and Kenny in another, and Steph and Janet got their own tent too. Once the tents were up, the next assignment was helping Kenny and Zac dig the latrine. "Dig it about 12 by 12 inches wide but only 8 inches deep." Mr. Barrett explained. "If you dig it any deeper, it won't decompose." Steph remembered learning about decomposition in science but didn't know that the bacteria that helps things decompose is only in the top eight inches of the soil. "Also," Mr. Barrett instructed, "You need to dig it away from the water and *please,* not close to the tents! We don't want to catch a whiff of that during the night!" The kids all laughed and headed into the forest to find the perfect spot for the toilet.

Their days on Shoshone Lake were filled with fishing, canoeing, playing in the cold water, and hiking. For breakfast, they ate cold cereal in little boxes that could be cut into bowls, peanut butter and jelly sandwiches for lunch and each night they had a big campfire and roasted hot dogs or cooked tinfoil dinners as well as any fish they had caught that day. There were also lots of snacks for them to munch on throughout the day like jerky, dried fruit, and trail mix. Steph's mom sent a big box of apples for fresh fruit and Janet's mom sent a huge bag of cheesy popcorn. The kids discovered the fish enjoyed the cheesy popcorn more than they did.

One day while fishing from the canoe, Mr. Barrett showed Steph and Janet how to gut a fish. He took his sharp knife and cut up the belly from the tail all the way to the head. Then opened the fish and in one motion tore out its entire insides. Birds were flying in circles above them, so Mr. Barrett tossed the guts into the air and a bird caught them and gulped them down. The girls were amazed and wanted to try it. Steph caught the next fish and did exactly as she had been shown. It worked! All the guts came out together! But as she stood up to throw the innards into the sky, she tipped the canoe completely over. All three of them went in! Laughter echoed throughout the lake, in fact, Steph laughed so hard she was pretty sure she peed her pants, but of course, no one could tell.

At night, the kids would lay awake in their sleeping bags talking and laughing back and forth between their tents until one of the dads would call for them to be quiet and go to sleep. Then they would giggle even more. Steph couldn't imagine a more wonderful trip and told her father she hoped they could come back every year for the rest of her life.

The last night of their trip was her tenth birthday. After dinner, her father brought out a small, wrapped gift for Steph to open by the fire. It looked and felt like a book. She imagined it must be *More Adventures of the Great Brain* so they could read together. She quickly tore off the wrapping paper. It *was* a book, but the title was, *My Diary* and it was filled with blank pages. "It's for you to write your own story," her father said with a smile, then added, "Maybe someday you will let me read it?" Steph was excited. She had never had a diary before. Maybe someday she *would* write a book and become a famous author?

Mr. Barnes suddenly took out his harmonica and started playing silly songs. They sang, laughed, told scary stories, and made smores around the campfire until it was very late. Steph wanted to hang on to the night forever.

At last, everyone started to feel sleepy, and they let the fire die down. Climbing into their tents, Steph and Janet decided they were too tired to brush their teeth and promised they would brush extra good tomorrow. Just as Steph was dosing off, one of the dads started snoring like a chain saw.

She giggled.

Thinking it must have woke Janet up too she whispered, "Hey you awake?" When Janet didn't answer she decided to get out her flashlight and her new diary. She took off the pen that was looped on the side and opened to the first blank page. After scribbling some little circles, the ink started to work and she wrote, August 22, 1969. I just turned ten years old today and I'm celebrating my birthday on Shoshone Lake with Janet, Zac and Kenny.

She paused, thinking deeply. Since meeting Janet, it was so much easier to ignore the teasing because now she had a best friend who understood her. Steph recalled the many times she had wondered how she would ever survive school and now, even though she worried about what fifth grade might bring, she was looking forward to the future rather than dreading it. She also knew there were other girls like her and maybe, just maybe, someday they would all get the chance to play!

She took a breath and continued to write, "I never thought I would feel this way, but I like my life and I'm glad I'm a tomboy. I wouldn't want to be anyone else!"

Author's afterword

In 1972, Title IX, a federal civil rights law was passed in the United States. This prohibited gender-based discrimination in any school or education program that received federal money. At the time I was thirteen years old and didn't know all of what this law meant, but I did understand that no girl should ever hear the words again, ***"You can't play, you're a girl."***

Title IX didn't suddenly make everything better for female athletes. Overcoming narrow-minded attitudes, stereotyping and bias was an ongoing challenge but it was a beginning. I will never forget the day when for the first time as a freshman in high school, I put on a girl's athletic uniform and played in a *real* game with *real* referees. Words cannot express how thrilled I was to be a part of a girls' team! My deepest appreciation goes out to all those who worked so hard to make women's athletics a reality for me, my daughters and now my granddaughters.

So much has been accomplished in the days since then, but so much more needs to be done in the world of humanity regarding gender, race and creed. We all do not share the same talents, but we all should have the equal opportunity to develop our talents whatever they may be.

# BASKETBALL